D1581003

Down's Syndrome and Dementia

Diana Kerr

VENTURE PRESS

Published by
VENTURE PRESS
16 Kent Street
Birmingham
B5 6RD

British Library Cataloguing-in-Publication Data
A catalogue record for this book is available from the British Library

ISBN 1 86178 017 6 (paperback)

Design, layout and production by
Hucksters Advertising & Publishing Consultants,
Riseden, Tidebrook, Wadhurst, East Sussex TN5 6PA

Cover design by:
Western Arts
194 Goswell Road
London
EC1V 7DT

Printed and bound in Great Britain by
Biddles Ltd, Guildford and King's Lynn

Contents

Useful addresses

Down's Syndrome Association
155 Mitcham Road
London SW17 9PG
Tel 0181 682 4001

Scottish Down's Syndrome Association
158/160 Balgreen Road
Edinburgh EH11 3AU
Tel 0131 313 4225

Alzheimer's Disease Society
Gordon House
10 Greencoat Place
London SWIP IPH

Alzheimers Scotland – Action on Dementia
8 Hill St
Edinburgh EH2 3JZ

Introduction

Judith is a 49-year-old woman with a dual diagnosis of Down's syndrome and
   dementia. Since the death of her mother four years ago she has lived with her
   older sister and her family.
Judith has lost much of her ability to communicate through the use of language.
   She has started to throw things in temper and on two recent occasions hurt one
   of her sister's children when pushing them out of her way. She has started to
   leave the house without telling anyone and was recently missing for two hours.
When in the house on her own with her sister Judith is her usual pleasant
   engaging personality, but she becomes easily agitated when other people arrive.
   This is particularly the case towards the latter part of the afternoon. This is also
   the time that the children return from school.
Judith has been attending an Adult Training Centre since she moved into the area
   to be with her sister. The staff are concerned by Judith's behaviour. They report
   that she becomes more agitated at meal times and has on a few occasions
   thrown her food. She has also started wandering outside the building and has
   been incontinent of urine.
Judith's sister feels exhausted and overwhelmed by the increasing demands made
   on her and feels that whilst some services may be withdrawn others, more
   appropriate to Judith's needs, are not available locally.

**Increasingly social workers find themselves involved
in making decisions for and with people like Judith:
in enabling relatives to make decisions and develop
coping strategies, and in supporting and advising care
staff in community, residential and day care services.**
They are often left feeling overwhelmed and under-
informed about the nature of either Down's syndrome or
dementia. Many social workers will have worked with
people with learning disabilities but will have little or no
experience of dementia. Others who have worked with
older people will have knowledge and experience of
working with people with dementia but know little about
people with learning disabilities. Both groups have much
to learn from each other.

   The intention of this book is to bring these two areas
together to help workers develop a better understanding
of the specific needs of people who have both diagnoses.

An increasing number of people will have both Down's syndrome and dementia. This has implications both for direct practitioners and for service providers. Without a clear understanding of the specific needs of this group service developers cannot plan effectively nor can they hope to avoid the present trend of misplacing people like Judith because suitable environments are not available.

INFORMATION ABOUT PEOPLE WITH DOWN'S SYNDROME

- Down's syndrome is a disorder which is the result of the inheritance of a third copy of all or part of chromosome 21.
- It is the most common cause of developmental delay, intellectual impairment and learning disability.
- Between 600 and 1000 live births a year have Down's syndrome. The variation is due to trends in maternal age at birth and selective terminations.

The first definitive description of Down's syndrome was made in 1866 by John Langdon Haydon Down. He identified the major phenotypic characteristics most commonly associated with the syndrome.

Since then there has been an abundance of material documenting the syndrome's various manifestations. For the purposes of this guide it is not necessary to list all the characteristics associated with the syndrome, but the following list does encompass some of the most common physical features:

- Flat back of the head
- Abundant neck skin
- Flat facial appearance
- Slanted eyes
- Epicanthic folds
- Small teeth
- Furrowed tongue
- High arched palate
- Short broad hands
- Curved fifth finger
- Four-finger crease on the palm
- A wide space between the first and second toes
- Speckling of the iris
- Congenital heart defects
- Gastro-intestinal abnormalities
- Muscle hypotonia
- Hyperextensibility or hyperflexibility
- Cervical spine instability
- Shortness of stature, at the bottom end of the range

The various characteristics described are not necessarily always present and where they are they will vary in degree; consequently when making a clinical diagnosis for Down's syndrome this will be based on the overall impression or gestalt rather than the existence of particular features.

There are some conditions which, although not confined to adults, are more likely to occur in the older age group.

Given the remit of this guide these are especially important to note. They are:

- Hypothyroidism
- Cataracts
- Hearing loss
- Changes in the knee and hip joints
- Spine disturbance
- Susceptibility to infections
- Sleep disturbance
- Mitral valve prolapse

DOWN'S SYNDROME AND LIFE EXPECTANCY

The life expectancy of people with Down's syndrome has increased dramatically over the last 50 years. In 1929 in England the average life expectancy was 9 years, and by 1949 this had increased to 12 years. Today about 80% of people with Down's syndrome live to over 50 years and some even survive into their late sixties or early seventies.

The increase in life expectancy is the result of a number of developments:

- The use of antibiotics
- The development of immunisation programmes
- The development and use of heart surgery to correct the congenital heart defects that affect 40-50% of people with Down's syndrome
- The move away from institutional care and the development of community care provision both in people's own homes and in supported accommodation.

No two people with Down's syndrome are the same, for they are individuals with highly varied abilities and personalities. Just like people without Down's syndrome, they are the product of their life experience, history and cultural expectations as well as their genetic inheritance.

What is dementia?

There are a number of different causes of dementia. The two most common are Alzheimer's disease and multi-infarct dementia. About 50% of people with dementia have the former and 25% have the latter. Some people also develop both.

> 'Dementia is a group of progressive diseases of the brain that slowly affect all functions of the mind and lead to deterioration in a person's ability to concentrate, remember and reason. It can affect every area of human thinking, feeling and behaviour.'
> **(Murphy 1986)**

For the purposes of this book we will be looking at Alzheimer's disease as this is the dementia to which people with Down's syndrome are susceptible. It should be noted, however, that people with Down's syndrome can also develop multi-infarct dementia or any other dementia in the same way as the general population.

Alzheimer's disease was first described by Alois Alzheimer in 1906. It is a disease which most commonly occurs in older people but does rarely also exist in younger adults and in particular in people with Down's syndrome in middle age.

It is caused by changes in the nerve cells of the brain. Plaques and neurofibrillary tangles develop which interfere with the transmission of signals from one neuron to another and from neuron to muscle. Once these changes have occurred they are irreversible

The disease progresses though the brain at varying rates and in varying patterns. As each part of the brain is damaged it is lost to function. It is important to note that some functions are found in more than one area of the brain, so elements of some functions may be retained to some degree for a while.

No two people will have an identical experience of the disease even when the same areas are affected.

THE BRAIN AND ITS FUNCTIONS

Social workers do not need to know the functions of all the different parts of the brain. What they do need to know is how the different functions are grouped. This helps in the understanding of specific behaviour and, more importantly, in the understanding of paradoxical behaviours. It also helps in making decisions about which skills and behaviour are to be encouraged and maintained and which are lost to function for ever.

Temporal Lobes These are located on either side of the brain. The left or dominant lobe (in people who are right-handed) stores verbal memory. The right side lobe stores visual memory. Smell and taste are located on both sides.

These lobes are involved in our ability to learn new things. Recent memory is laid down and is then moved back and stored deep inside the temporal lobes. With the onset of dementia damage occurs to the lobes and recent memory is lost. Frequently used and strongly stored memories will remain for some time, but as the disease progresses these too will be lost.

Pareital lobes These are also located on either side of the brain, with each side having a specific function.

The left side is the analytical and logical centre and is the area that controls patterning. It is, therefore, important in our use of language – which involves the patterning of words – in our ability to do arithmetic and hence manage money, and in our understanding of the pattern or geography of our body. This lobe tells us which is our right side and which our left – critical information when dressing.

When this lobe is damaged people will have difficulty constructing sentences and with reading and writing. They will also have difficulty with dressing. This is important for carers to know, because once the ability to remember patterns has gone no amount of explaining or showing will get the patterns back. There will come a point, for example, when the person can no longer dress themselves. However, it may be that the person can remember two patterns but not three, so one needs to be cautious in deciding when all function has gone.

The right side lobe is our three-dimensional centre. This tells us where we are in space and helps us to get

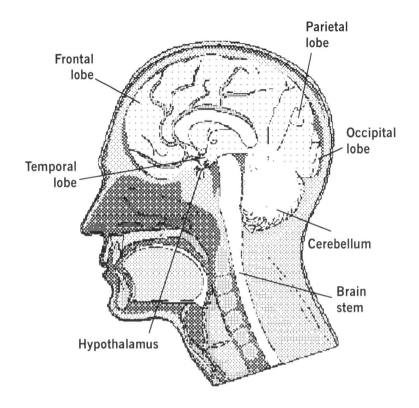

around our environment. Once this is damaged people will have difficulty in locating themselves and in making sense of their surroundings. In particular they will have difficulty in seeing changes of levels and will often misinterpret changes in texture and colour, seeing steps where there are none and not seeing those that are there. **Frontal lobes** These are where new learning takes place before being passed back into the parietal lobes. This is our planning and organising centre. Importantly in understanding some behaviour seen in Alzheimer's disease, it is also where our initiator is. This is the part which gets us going to do things. When this is damaged people may sit and do nothing, not because they cannot but because their initiator cannot get them going. If someone else takes the role of initiator then the person will engage in activity. One problem, however, is that once the person has started to do something the initiator does not switch off automatically and they may continue to do the same thing over and over again (perseveration) until prompted into doing something else.

These lobes are also where we store our knowledge of socially appropriate behaviour.

Limbic region This controls sleep, appetite and emotions. It can be disrupted when the frontal and temporal lobes are affected.

Cerebellum This controls balance and the co-ordination of voluntary movements such as walking and sitting.

Hypothalamus This is the first part of the brain to be damaged by Alzheimer's disease. It is very important to memory and learning.

Note that functions are not necessarily restricted to one area of the brain. Those functions that are related to memory, for example, are located in a number of areas.

Although the damage is irreversible it is characteristic of people with dementia to be more receptive some days than others and even to change throughout the course of a day. This may in part be because of an on-off impulse in the transmission of signals in the cell, or simply because the person has fewer resources to call on, so is much more likely to be affected by factors such as tiredness, stress, anxiety and physical illness. For people with Down's syndrome, who may have fewer resources in terms of concentration span and adaptive skills to start with, this may be even more marked.

PROGRESSION OF THE DISEASE

You will sometimes come across references to 'stages of dementia'. These are described as mild, moderate and severe. Various characteristics are attributed to each stage. This is not necessarily helpful as it implies that people go through each stage completely and that if they have some characteristics of a particular stage then the rest will soon follow. This is not the case.

People with dementia are individuals with their own personalities, past experiences and coping strategies. As with any illness, Alzheimer's disease will be experienced differently by different people and it is therefore essential to be cautious about making hard and fast statements about its progression.

It is important to see the illness as a progression with each person travelling at their own speed and with different coping mechanisms. A useful way to look at the illness is as a series of gradual losses. This counteracts the tendency to compartmentalise the various developments. (When looking specifically at the disease in people with Down's syndrome there is perhaps a need to consider the possibility of more distinct stages, but the following model is nevertheless useful.)

ALZHEIMER'S DISEASE: THE GRADUAL LOSSES

Forgetfulness

Word-finding problems

Mild confusion

Anxiety

Mild personality changes

Depression

Inability to learn new things

Paranoid thoughts

Increasing memory problems

Obsessional behaviours

Repetitive questioning

Problems with making decisions

Disorientation in time, place and person

Reservation

Decreasing communication

Loss of forward planning

Problems with self care

Decreased independence in activities of daily living

Poor problem solving

Agitation, restlessness and wandering

Incontinence problems

Behavioural problems

Sleep disturbances

Falls

Language loss and communication problems

Loss of identity

Extreme disorientation

Confined to bed

Extreme confusion

No communication

Double incontinence

Major loss of all functioning

No mobility

Death

(Gardner 1993)

The physical changes listed below tend to occur in the later stages:

● Weight loss	● Tremor
● Self-neglect	● Epileptiform seizures
● Malnutrition	● Rigidity
● Incontinence	● Instability
● Receptive and expressive dysphasia	● Visual spatial problems
● General slowing down	● Immobility

UNDERSTANDING PARADOXICAL BEHAVIOURS

Look again at the diagram of the brain. Because different parts of the brain have different functions and because different parts are affected at different times, there can be considerable variations in function. It can also be difficult for a care giver and indeed an assessor to determine the person's true level of functioning. If, for example, the part of the brain that processes speech and word recognition is damaged, then asking someone to close the door may have no effect. However, only a minute later, the person may very well close the door themselves, in response to feeling a bit cold. This is because they are responding to messages in another part of the brain. This can be very difficult to cope with and there is a temptation to think that the person is being awkward or stubborn.

Similarly someone may well be able to locate themselves in a room and have a clear sense of its geography but not be able to dress themselves. This is because the part of the brain which tells them which is their right side and which their left, that is the geography of their body, has been damaged. This can be very frustrating for care givers because no matter how often they explain or demonstrate how to dress, the person will never be able to get it right because that part of the brain is lost to function forever.

Remember that even the apparently simplest of everyday tasks may well use the functions of a number of areas of the brain.

The link between Down's syndrome and dementia

Whilst there are a number of different dementias, the type of dementia associated with Down's syndrome is specifically Alzheimer's disease. The existence of a link between Down's syndrome and Alzheimer's disease was first noted in 1948 (Jervis 1948). However the nature of the link was not established until much later, as increasing amounts of research were carried out in the 1970s and 1980s.

As more people with Down's syndrome were living to middle age the development of Alzheimer's disease was noted. It was found at post mortem that almost everyone with Down's syndrome over the age of 40 years had developed the neuropathological features characteristic of Alzheimer's disease. What is particularly interesting is that despite the existence of these physical features only some people had developed the clinical features of Alzheimer's disease in their lifetime.

The most favoured explanation of the link is that the existence of the extra chromosome 21 causes the production of a particular protein, called Beta-Amyloid protein. This is found in the neurofibrillary tangles associated with Alzheimer's disease.

There is, however, some debate about the exact role of this protein. The suggestion is that other factors may be involved. Certainly there is no direct link between the existence of deposits of the protein and the onset of Alzheimer's disease.

Owens, Dawson and Losin (1971), while accepting that the disease is genetically determined in people with Down's syndrome, argue that there may well be precipitating factors. They suggest that

'trauma, living conditions and pre-psychotic personality... in conjunction with the ability of the individual brain to compensate for organic changes as well as the level of integration achieved by the organism, may also be contributory factors.'

It is clear, however, that there is a link between chromosome 21 and Alzheimer's disease in people with Down's syndrome. More research will need to be carried out before definitive statements can be made and certainly before any type of treatment to interfere with the disease process can be developed.

Despite the fact that almost everyone with Down's syndrome develops the characteristic tangles of Alzheimer's disease by the time they are 40 years, the average age of onset of the clinical features is 54.2 years. It is unclear why there is this significant delay, which is not characteristic of the general population.

There is no national statistic which indicates the prevalence of Alzheimer's disease amongst people with Down's syndrome, but there have been a number of studies from which, perhaps, one could extrapolate. The problem is that there are considerable variations in the findings, which may well be the result of the difficulties experienced in determining a definite diagnosis. However, research on age-specific prevalence rates indicates that in the 35-49 age group 8% developed the disease; in the 50-59 age group 55% developed it; and in the over-60-year-olds there was a 75% prevalence (Lai and Williams 1989).

What is important is the fact that there is no inevitability about the onset of the disease, and that even the most pessimistic study suggests that not every person with Down's syndrome will develop the clinical symptoms of Alzheimer's disease.

Differential diagnosis

> Margaret is 45 years old. She has Down's syndrome. Two years ago she moved into supported accommodation following her mother's admission to residential care and her father's own declining health.
>
> Margaret already had many daily living skills, but over this period she has managed to acquire a new level of independence. She has become more responsible for her own hygiene needs. She has learned to use the washing machine and organise her own bathing routine. She has also been able to cook simple meals with staff support. She has formed ready friendships with the other tenants in the house.
>
> About three weeks ago Margaret appeared to become increasingly restless and confused. She has neglected her bathing routine and has actually started to smell rather badly, especially of urine. She has also become a bit withdrawn and quarrelsome with the other people living in the house. Contrary to her normal behaviour she also recently hit out at another tenant who she accused of eating her food.

If Margaret's case study is compared to Judith's at the beginning of this book, or even to the list of symptoms and characteristics commonly associated with Alzheimer's disease on page 9, you will undoubtedly see many similarities that could well lead you to make a diagnosis of Alzheimer's disease.

This would be incorrect.

Certainly Margaret has many of the characteristic behaviours associated with the disease. One particular aspect, however, is not typical – the speed of onset. With Alzheimer's disease such changes would not have occurred over such a short period but would have taken months or even years to develop.

Margaret actually had an **Acute Confusional State** caused by a treatable urinary tract infection. After a few days of treatment she was back to her usual self.

This example serves to illustrate the critical importance of ruling out other causes of confusion.

An Acute Confusional State is just that: acute. It develops quickly and is treatable. It can be caused by many different factors which upset the person's normal physical or mental well-being.

Below is a list of the most common causes of Acute Confusional States. Some of them are particularly significant for people with Down's syndrome and these will be covered in greater detail later on.

● Toxicity	This can be caused by wrong dosages or mixing drugs incorrectly. People with Down's syndrome are particularly susceptible to folic acid abnormalities as a result of taking anti-convulsants
● Infections	Most common causes are urinary tract and chest infections
● Endocrine and metabolic disturbances	e.g. hypothyroidism, diabetes
● Heart disease	
● Renal failure	
● Bone fractures	Fractured hips are the most common
● Constipation	
● Poor diet	May cause malnutrition and anaemia
● Excess alcohol	
● Lack of sleep	
● Sensory impairment	Poor eyesight, hearing loss, social isolation
● Environmental changes	
● Grief reactions	

If someone has a sudden onset Confusional State all of the above should be considered. When working with people with Down's syndrome there are some which need particular attention:

- ● Toxicity
- ● Hypothyroidism
- ● Sensory impairment
- ● Grief reactions and environmental changes
- ● Lack of sleep

TOXICITY

People with Down's syndrome in their fifties are more susceptible to the adverse effects of particular combinations and types of medication. The use of both prescribed and over the counter drugs can lead to cognitive impairment and confusion, as can polypharmacy, that is the use of multiple drugs.

Of particular relevance to people with Down's syndrome is the use of anti-convulsants, which can lead to folic acid abnormalities. Some of the newer drugs, such as Vigabatrim, may have a positive effect on the seizures but often cause considerable behavioural deterioration.

HYPOTHYROIDISM

Hypothyroidism occurs in 20-30% of people with Down's syndrome. The manifestations of hypothyroidism are:

- Lethargy
- Functional decline
- Confusion
- Constipation
- Dry skin
- Fatigue
- Depression

Clearly the combination of these changes can easily look like dementia, but it is vital that the true cause is recognised because if this goes untreated it could lead to hallucinations and coma.

SENSORY IMPAIRMENT

People with Down's syndrome are susceptible to age-related illnesses such as cataracts at an earlier stage than the general population. Up to 40% of people with Down's syndrome develop cataracts (Hiles et al 1990). Hearing loss is also a characteristic of people with Down's syndrome. Sensory impairment may cause people to misunderstand what is going on around them, and they may well become frustrated and even aggressive. This level of impairment can lead to functional and behavioural deterioration that can easily be misinterpreted as Alzheimer's disease. As a consequence of their condition being wrongly diagnosed, the person may well experience changes in their environment and also in staff expectations, and this will only exacerbate the situation.

GRIEF REACTIONS AND ENVIRONMENTAL CHANGES

It is important to remember that many people in their forties and fifties will be likely to lose parents. Their change in behaviour may well be the result of grieving. They may also have lost the person that they relied on to fill in the gaps in their memory and to orientate them when necessary. If the observed behaviour is not understood in this context then a wrong assessment will result and the person may experience further disruption and consequent losses. This is a common occurrence. Maureen Oswin in her book *'Am I Allowed to Cry?'* details the way in which people with learning disabilities experience multiple moves after the loss of a carer:

'Some people with learning difficulties have as many as five different residential placements during the first year after a bereavement.'

(Oswin 1991, p. 83)

Very often there is also an assumption that the person who has died was covering up for the person and so masking the existence and level of the dementia.

The loss may well be through staff changes. Even if there has been preparation for the departure of a member of staff this will not remove the sense of loss.

LACK OF SLEEP

People with Down's syndrome are particularly prone to sleep apnoea, the temporary lack of breathing during sleep, and a general lack of sleep. This can lead to:

- Excessive daytime inactivity
- Behaviour disturbance
- Failure to thrive
- Decline in functional skills
- Disruptive sleep patterns

Because we know that people in their late forties and early fifties are at risk of developing Alzheimer's disease there may well be a tendency to see the often dramatic and confused behaviour as evidence of its presence rather than the consequence of disturbed sleep patterns.

DEPRESSION

There are a number of conditions other than Acute Confusional States which can be, and often are, confused with Alzheimer's disease. The one that is most important to consider is depression.

Many symptoms that are associated with Alzheimer's disease are also found in people with Down's syndrome who are depressed.

> *'Studies have found that depressive affect and cognitions are often indirectly expressed by individuals with Down's syndrome, with the most common symptoms including aggressive acting out, withdrawal, somatic complaints, increased dependency, irritability and disturbances of vegetative function.'*
>
> **(Aylward, Burt, Thorpe, Lai & Dalton 1995)**

People with hypothyroidism are susceptible to depression. The experience of loss that might be the result of the loss of a loved one but equally may be the result of moving from hospital to the community or of staff changes could cause a reactive depression.

Obviously it is not the job of the social worker to make a formal diagnosis but there are some important and useful pointers to be aware of:

The person with depression	The person with Alzheimer's disease
● Often complains of poor memory	● Is often unaware of memory problems
● May say 'I don't know' in answer to questions which require thought or concentration	● Will 'confabulate' or make up answers to questions which require concentration or good memory and appears unaware that the answer is incorrect
● Shows fluctuating ability and uneven impairment on cognitive testing	● Tends to show consistent global impairment on cognitive testing
● Gives up easily, is poorly motivated and uninterested	● Has a go
● May be slow but successful in any complex task, is aware of errors.	● Unsuccessful in carrying out tasks which require concentration, appears unaware of errors.

If you look at the indicators given in the box on the previous page for the person with Alzheimer's disease, you will appreciate that making the necessary distinction between depression and Alzheimer's disease may be much more difficult with a person with Down's syndrome than it is in the general population.

Finally it should be borne in mind that it is possible to have an Acute Confusional State or depression as well as Alzheimer's disease. If someone already has a diagnosis of Alzheimer's disease it may be tempting to see a sudden change and increase in confusion as a sign that the disease is progressing more rapidly, rather than as the direct result of an infection or trauma. This is especially important to remember when working with people with Down's syndrome and Alzheimer's disease, where there may be more abrupt changes than in the general population.

Diagnosing Alzheimer's disease in people with Down's syndrome

Assessing people with Down's syndrome for Alzheimer's disease is far more complicated and difficult than for the general population. There are a number of reasons for this:

- Assessment tools used to determine Alzheimer's disease assume that the person had a previously intact level of cognitive functioning. One study of 116 assessment tools found that 'not one could be used in isolation for the population who also have intellectual impairment' (Koenig 1995).
- There is often no single documentation of previous abilities. Clearly if there is not an established baseline then it is difficult to measure deterioration. Equally it is pointless to ask someone to complete a task that they have never previously mastered.
- Early memory loss and communication problems frequently get masked. Carers and staff will often fail to appreciate the very small initial changes in the person and attribute their difficulties to poor language skills in particular and the learning disability in general.

The consequence of this is that often by the time a diagnosis is made the person with Down's syndrome is at a more advanced stage of the illness than the general population is at the point of diagnosis.

To carry out an effective assessment, therefore, there needs to be an assessment of previous abilities to try to establish a baseline against which to measure changes. Carers' knowledge as well as previous documentation such as care plans and action plans play a vital role here.

There then needs to be a process of monitoring changes over a period. The carer is critical in this process, but they must be informed of the things to look out for and note.

Because of the complex nature of the assessment and because of the multiple needs of the person with Down's syndrome and Alzheimer's disease, it is essential that a multi-disciplinary team is involved in this process. This team should involve:

- Carers
- G.P.
- Community nurse
- Psychologist
- Psychiatrist with special knowledge of learning disabilities
- Physiotherapist
- Occupational therapist
- Social worker.

The list above highlights the fact that people with Down's syndrome and Alzheimer's disease have some significantly different needs from the general population with Alzheimer's disease.

These differences tend to be around three key areas:

- Observed features in the **early stage** of the illness
- The characteristics of the illness in the **mid, late** and **end stages**
- The **duration** of the illness.

THE EARLY STAGE

The most frequently reported features in the early stages of Alzheimer's disease are:

- Seizures. Note that this is distinctly different from the general population who, if they do develop seizures, develop them in the latter part of the illness. Studies suggest that over 80% of people with Down's syndrome and Alzheimer's disease will experience seizure activity. The seizures will start, on average, 2 1/2 years from the onset of the dementia
- Apathy and general inactivity
- Short term memory loss
- Loss of daily living skills
- Loss of amenability and sociability
- Loss of interest in favoured hobbies
- Withdrawal of spontaneous communication
- Loss of road sense. Note that in the general population this skill remains for a long time
- Disorientation and confusion
- Loss of comprehension
- Increased wandering.

Very often these changes go unnoticed until after some crisis or change of circumstances. It is not uncommon to hear that it was after a holiday that the carer noticed an apparent sudden change. Similarly other changes such as the move from hospital to community or the loss of a key person in their life may cause the person to become more disorientated, withdrawn and apathetic. Of course the problem for accurate assessment is that these types of changes can also cause an Acute Confusional State, so it is important to note whether there had already been insidious changes that had gone unremarked.

If someone exhibits two or more of these characteristics it does not necessarily mean that they have Alzheimer's disease. It does, however, indicate a need for a full and systematic assessment.

EARLY STAGE PRACTICES

Once a diagnosis has been made the carers need to be informed and offered counselling and training. Support staff should also be given specific training. It is also important to be clear about what and how you tell the person with dementia. They have a right, if they are able, to make statements about what they want for their future. They may well want to appoint a named person to make decisions for them and act as their advocate.

In the early stages it is crucial to maintain as many routines and activities as possible. Contact with the community and the work place should be actively supported. This may involve negotiations with the work place or the day centre, where adjustments to some of the more stress-inducing aspects of the routines may require adjustment. Some day centres provide a quieter space and opportunities for the person with Alzheimer's disease to eat somewhere other than the cafeteria, which is often a hive of activity and noise.

There should be a concentration on preferred and achievable activities. These help maintain a sense of involvement and achievement which will in turn enhance a person's sense of well-being and positive self esteem. This is extremely important at this stage as people become increasingly aware of their diminishing abilities. Attention should also be given to developing activities which help to maintain muscle tone and strength. Dancing is an excellent way to achieve this.

As in the later stages, the emphasis should be on adapting environments to the individual and not the other way round.

THE MID AND LATER STAGES

A characteristic of the progression of Alzheimer's disease amongst people with Down's syndrome is that there are often quite sudden and profound changes. However, as indicated earlier, the symptoms may appear at different times in different people. The following is a list of characteristics most often reported in the later stages of the illness in people with Down's syndrome:

- Loss of mobility
- Depression
- Hallucinations
- Delusions
- Irrational fears
- Swearing
- Incontinence
- Verbal aggression
- Physical aggression

(Dalton, Seltzer, Adlin and Wisnieski 1993)

MID STAGE PRACTICES

There may be a loss of self-care skills and developing incontinence. There may also be dramatic personality changes and the onset of seizures. Mobility decreases and memory loss becomes more marked. It now becomes especially important to validate the person and not force them to see the world from the carer's perspective. Because of these changes there is an increased need to adapt the environment. This can lead not only to increased expenditure and financial stress but can highlight the dilemmas around conflicting needs.

Consider the following:

Martin is 51 years old, he has Down's yndrome and was diagnosed with Alzheimer's disease 2 1/2 years ago. He lives in a supported tenancy with three other men. He shares a room with one of them. He has known one member of staff for 15 years. Four months ago he started to lose his speech rapidly. He became much less mobile, often finding the use of the stairs too difficult. He became less able to take himself to the toilet and needed assistance with his meals. The voluntary organisation who supported Martin employed extra staff to try to meet Martin's needs. It became increasingly clear that there needed to be a more radical approach to the situation. Martin's room-mate was increasingly disturbed by the changes in Martin and clearly needed a room to himself. It was also evident that Martin needed a downstairs bedroom and a toilet adapted to his needs. The house was not big enough to have a downstairs room converted.

The staff saw three options:

> 1 Move Martin into residential/nursing care provision for older people with dementia
> 2 Have an extension built to provide a bedroom with en suite bathroom
> 3 Move the entire household to another more suitable house in the same location.

You could probably argue for any or none of these options. The staff seriously considered the second option but it was recognised that the constant noise and toing and froing of workmen as well as the inevitable changes to the existing structure of the building would cause anxiety and distress for Martin. The third option was the preferred one for Martin because it could be handled at his pace and all the staff and tenants would remain the same. Of course this may very well not have been the preferred option of the other tenants! The staff were not prepared to consider the possibility of Martin going into care.

Many would argue that given the complex nature of the disease in this particular group of people what is required is a separate service which would provide hospice-type care, particularly in the later stages. If this is the case then there are other critical questions that need to be addressed. When, for example, should someone be moved? If this is done too early they may be needlessly denied the familiarity and comfort of their own home. Left too late and the person may not receive the most appropriate support and care.

The provision of additional supports and respite may enable a carer to continue supporting the person at home. For the person with dementia this is the best thing, so all attempts should be made to support the carer and meet their needs.

Sometimes at this stage the strain becomes too great and a change of residence may be needed. It is essential that the social worker is able to assess the suitability of possible provision. No matter what the setting, the focus at this stage should be the maintenance of skills and the preservation of health. Every attempt should be made to minimise agitation and aid orientation. Wandering will often occur. Attempts should be made to understand its meaning and significance. The provision of wandering paths and cues for orientation should be used.

Special attention needs to be paid to nutrition. It is important to provide food when the person is most receptive and willing to eat:

- Try to make the meal that is most likely to be eaten the one that is the most nourishing
- Create a calm atmosphere and reduce stimuli at meal times
- Give the person time to eat and if necessary provide finger foods
- The use of music and aroma should be considered as appropriate.

Because of decreasing mobility there is an increased risk of constipation, and urinary tract and chest infections.

Incontinence problems can be lessened by making toilets easily accessible.

THE END STAGE

A review study of 20 adults who had Alzheimer's disease and Down's syndrome found that in the end stage of the illness, that is six months prior to death, there were a number of characteristics which were common to them all. At this terminal stage there was

'severe intellectual deterioration, marked personality and mood changes, loss of sphincter control, seizure

activity, immobility with hypertonia and complete loss of self-care skills.'

(Prasher 1995)

These findings are confirmed elsewhere (Dawson 1994). People also lose the ability to sit up, chew or swallow. Inevitably medical intervention increases at this stage.

Clearly this pattern of symptoms and the fact that there are often sudden changes associated with people with Down's syndrome and Alzheimer's disease requires frequent reviews and a flexible, responsive service directed to the particular needs of this group.

LATE STAGE PRACTICES
At this stage there is a loss of basic skills such as eating and drinking. This, combined with changes in the metabolism, leads to weight loss. The weight loss and lack of mobility leads to the development of skin pressure sores. There is also an increased risk of dehydration, choking and aspirant pneumonia. Clearly there needs to be a greater emphasis on the person's medical needs.

Although almost all verbal ability is lost by this stage, there are often residual phrases and words. These should be given special attention.

Of course a major concern at this stage is to support staff and carers in coming to terms with the dying and eventual death.

THE DURATION OF THE DISEASE
The duration of Alzheimer's disease in the general population is generally between 8 and 15 years, and occasionally 20 years. In the population with Down's syndrome the time between diagnosis and death can be as short as 3-5 years, although for reasons already given the diagnosis may well have come some time after actual onset of the symptoms.

Because of the speed of the development it is critical that diagnosis is made as early as possible. This will allow for multi-disciplinary interventions to be developed and plans to be made.

Finally, whilst the data suggests that there are subtle and substantial differences between people with Down's syndrome and Alzheimer's disease and the general population with Alzheimer's disease, some of these differences may be the result not of pathological differences but of the variation in skills and abilities available to both groups. The variations may also be because of the difficulties in collecting data on a group whose disabilities may mask aspects of the disease.

Assessment of need

The NHS and Community Care Act (1990) states that the purpose of assessment is:

'To analyse a person's situation, determine their care needs and relate these needs to options for meeting them.'

Clearly this statement demands that the client's needs are paramount and that they should not simply be assessed for existing and available services.

These needs require that the assessor focus as much on the person's retained skills, strengths and abilities as on their dependency needs and disabilities.

Once the label of dementia has been applied there can follow a process of negative responses which very easily lead to the identification of the person's disabilities and dependencies with little attempt to define what they can still achieve. This is

'reinforced by low expectations of staff and the assumption that the client cannot do much.'

(Burton, Chapman and Myers 1997)

In this the authors are referring to the general population with Alzheimer's disease. How much greater is the potential for negative responses to people with Down's syndrome who already are seen as less able and more dependent? This is particularly relevant when they may have greater difficulty in communicating their needs.

Before considering the assessment process it is important to state the following principles which should inform both the process of the assessment and the matching of resources:

- The person with the dual diagnosis has the same basic needs as anyone else. There are, however, some particular needs to which social workers must pay particular attention.
- Any assessment of need must cover the four domains of human functioning, physical, intellectual, emotional and social. To fail to do this is to fail to see their common humanity.

Additionally the person needs:

- Consistent and predictable environments
- To be maintained for as long as possible in their familiar environment
- Us to modify our behaviour and not expect them to modify theirs
- Us to try to understand their reality and not demand that they enter ours when this is too difficult
- To be helped to retain their skills and freedoms for as long as possible
- Services which are tailored to meet their specific needs
- Us to see the person first and the disease second. This requires us to see their uniqueness and to recognise that everyone experiences the disease differently.

THE ASSESSMENT PROCESS

TIME SCALE

Whenever possible when assessing anyone with dementia, aim for an anticipated time scale of two to three weeks. This should involve at least three separate meetings which need to be made at different times of the day.

This is particularly critical to the development of care packages. If the assessment is carried out whilst the person is at their most confused, probably in the late afternoon, this could lead to an over-provision of service. This will undermine one of the main principles of working with people with dementia, that is to provide only for what they can't do and thus maintain skills for as long as possible. Conversely to assess when they are at their most lucid may expose them to under-provision and unnecessary risk.

COMMUNICATING WITH THE PERSON

At your meetings, make sure that you are introduced by someone who is familiar to the person. They may well be frightened of a stranger and not fully understand your role and purpose.

Attend to the environment to make sure that it enhances communication and does not inhibit or agitate the person (see relevant sections on **Communication** and **Creating a Therapeutic Environment**).

Be particularly attentive to the symbolic meaning of what the person says and give them plenty of time to process questions and work out a reply.

Be particularly aware of the difficulties and frustrations which may be caused by visual and hearing impairment. Always check that their glasses are clean and their hearing aid turned on.

INVOLVE THE PERSON

As far as possible make sure that everyone is involved and knows what is being decided and recorded. The person with Alzheimer's disease should be encouraged to make statements about their present and future needs. They may want to identify a named person to make decisions on their behalf when they are no longer able to do so.

Because of communication difficulties it is tempting to discuss the person's needs with carers and support staff and not give the person the time and space to express their needs. The communication process could and should form part of the assessment.

Use the professional and personal support network.

When working with people with Down's syndrome and Alzheimer's disease the worker will usually have to work with a wider range of professionals than would be the case when assessing the needs of someone from the general population. This is because the person with Down's syndrome will already be receiving services. The people most likely to be involved are:

Carers Obviously carers will have a great deal of information and insight into the needs of the person.

The community nurse Community nurses have increasingly developed their role in relation to people with learning disabilities. Many will have had a critical function in the multi-disciplinary learning disabilities team.

The psychiatrist It is important to use a psychiatrist who will have special knowledge of learning disabilities and, if a diagnosis of dementia has not been made, will be the necessary link to the psychogeriatrician who must make a diagnosis before dementia can be assumed.

Occupational therapists They may well be involved in the provision of adaptations.

Staff at the adult training centre/resource centre If the person is attending a centre it is important to have the assessment of the staff, as the person may exhibit different but significant behaviour in this particular setting.

Respite providers Many people with Down's syndrome will have been using respite resources, sometimes for many years. Staff will have useful information about changes in behaviour as well as an ability to identify needs.

Befrienders and volunteers Many people with Down's syndrome will have a befriender or volunteer worker. This person will also have information which may well be pertinent to the assessment. There is, of course, a need for caution as confidentiality and privacy must be respected.

RECOGNISE THE POTENTIAL CONFLICT OF INTERESTS

As the illness progresses the demands made on the carer will increase. The need for the carer to have respite may well come to outweigh the need of the person with Down's syndrome to be with the carer. Similarly, in supported accommodation the needs of other tenants may be in conflict with the needs of the person with Alzheimer's disease.

CARENAPD

In carrying out a standard comprehensive assessment most of the above points will be covered. There is, however, an assessment tool, 'CarenapD', developed by the Scottish Office and the Dementia Services Development Centre at Stirling University. This has been specifically designed for the assessment of need of people with dementia. It was not designed for people with Down's syndrome and Alzheimer's disease but with a few adaptations it is an extremely useful tool.

The particular relevance of Carenap D to the assessment of people with a dual diagnosis is that

'it has been designed from a multi-disciplinary perspective and it is suitable for use by all the relevant professions.'

(Carenap D User Notes 1994)

This means that all professionals will be using the same language and criteria.

The tool is divided into separate sections. The first contains a screening section, in which there are criteria that must be met before continuing with the asessment.

It focuses on all areas of potential difficulty and requires the assessor to determine the level of the person's needs and to what extent they are met, partially met or unmet. Where unmet need is identified there are eight possible types of help to choose from:

● Social stimulation/activity	Where someone provides company or activities
● Prompting/supervision	Where someone is there to ensure the person manages (prompting can be either verbal or physical)
● Physical assistance	Where a helper does tasks for the person
● Aids and adaptations	These could be for the person or the environment, and may include changing the environment (e.g. reducing stimulation)
● Specialist assessment	Where further assessment or help is required (e.g. medical, OT, psychological)
● Counselling for the person	To assist emotional coping
● Behaviour management	To deal with difficult behaviour
● Carer advice/training	For informal and formal carers, to help them help the person

(From Care Nap D User Notes 1994)

The tool also has a very important section which is specifically devoted to the needs of carers.

More information about Carenap D can be obtained from the Dementia Services Development Centre at the University of Stirling.

It is relevant here to consider two approaches involved in the decision-making process when assessing and providing resources for people who have dementia and Down's syndrome.

These two approaches are 'Best Interest' and 'Substituted Judgement'.

(Burton, Chapman and Myers 1997)

A 'best interest' approach is appropriate where there have always been doubts about a person's ability to make competent decisions. For most people who develop dementia this is actually generally inappropriate. But for a larger number of people with Down's syndrome this may be appropriate, although it will probably only apply to specific areas of competence.

A 'substituted judgement' approach is one that is designed to make sure that decisions are made in line with the person's known values, beliefs and desires when they were competent to make such decisions.

When trying to make decisions it can, in reality, be difficult to stick to a substituted judgement approach, especially if there are other people whose interests also need to be taken into account.

Communication

Communication is one of the main areas of difficulty in working with people with dementia. However, it is worth considering that if we sometimes feel frustrated and misunderstood, how much more overwhelmed must the person with dementia feel?

For most of us only 20% of our communication is verbal while 80% is non-verbal, that is touch, tone of voice, facial expression, gesture and body language. Someone with Down's syndrome may already have difficulty with verbal skills, and this is then exacerbated by the onset of Alzheimer's disease.

There are a number of communication problems which develop as the disease progresses. They can be categorised as follows:

●	Dysarthia	slurred speech
●	Aphasia	an inability to express language or to understand the spoken word. This is especially the case with words that are not commonly used or are highly abstract
●	Agnosia	loss of ability to recognise objects, either by name or sight
●	Apraxia	loss of ability to form purposeful movements. This can extend to the inability to remember the patterns used to form words.

When our ability to communicate verbally is impaired non-verbal communication becomes even more important. People with Alzheimer's disease become much more aware of the emotional content of an exchange. This can easily lead to severe communication difficulties, caused by the carer relying on verbal cues but the person with dementia responding to body language and facial expression.

Consider the following scenario:

Jamie, who has Down's syndrome and Alzheimer's disease, is sitting in the hall waiting for the bus to take him to the day centre. His support worker is standing close by. Jamie asks for her attention but she can see another tenant about to spill his tea. She tells Jamie she will be with him in just a minute and then goes over to the other tenant. Jamie starts to shout and taking his coat off says 'You are horrible, I don't like you, I'm not going on the bus'.

The worker has promised attention but what Jamie sees is her back turned towards him, and her body language is not mitigated by the words of attention actually spoken.

Carers will be familiar with similar situations where their words of concern have gone unnoticed but the stress in their face has caused an outburst because the person with dementia has interpreted this as anger.

The person is primarily responding to the perceived non-verbal cues.

Very often the person with Alzheimer's disease will not be able to find the right word but will express their feelings in a jumbled and incoherent way.

Care givers and workers need to be wary of taking what is said literally and should try to recognise the emotions behind the words. Failure to do so means that the emotional content of an interaction goes unacknowledged or misinterpreted.

Because the part of the brain that stores language is often affected early in the disease, language difficulties are often the first symptom of the illness. And because people with Down's syndrome may already have a reduced bank of words, this deficit will be even more profound.

These difficulties often mean that the person will use something that roughly describes the object, for example a bus may become *'the thing with wheels'*, or slippers *'the foot thing'*. Later emptier words will be used, so the piano becomes *'that thing'* or a carer becomes *'that person'*. But just because the language has become reduced this does not mean that the emotions behind it are any less intense.

It is important to remember that the person with Alzheimer's disease will feel increasingly out of control and confused by their environment. This will increase their stress levels which in turn makes finding the right word or phrase even more difficult. Even people with fully intact brains forget words and numbers when stressed. How much more difficult for someone with Down's syndrome and Alzheimer's disease?

It is essential therefore that all communication is conducted in as stress-free an environment as possible. This involves managing not only the physical environment but our own behaviours and unintended messages.

There are a number of do's and don'ts for developing a stress-free situation and aiding effective communication:

DO

- Find a quiet calming place
- Approach the person from the front and establish eye contact
- Try not to stare as this can be intimidating
- Smile once you are sure you have been seen
- Identify yourself and use their name
- Make sure they see you before you touch them. Remember that people with Down's syndrome often have a visual impairment and hearing loss so may not hear you approaching
- Try to talk to the person on your own
- Work out when the person is most able to concentrate and understand you, and if possible communicate important things then (remember that the effects of dementia vary during the course of the day)
- Speak a little more slowly than usual and as clearly as possible. Remember that people with Down's syndrome often have a hearing impairment
- Keep questions simple and only ask one question at a time
- Give specific choices which require yes or no answers. 'Do you want a cup of tea?', not 'What would you like to drink?'
- Give lots of reminders when you are giving information. For example, 'Your brother Bill is coming today'; 'Bill will take you out'
- Try to be direct and say what you mean. Don't say 'I can't be everywhere at once', try 'I will be with you soon'
- Use visual cues such as photographs
- Give the person more time to respond
- Prompt and gently remind them of the topic if they wander off. But do not insist
- Allow and even encourage the person to talk about the past. This is very often easier for the confused person. You can then link it to the present: 'You used to... Nowadays you...'
- Remember that the person with Down's syndrome and Alzheimer's disease may well have to rely on less complex language.

> **DON'T**
> - Try to communicate when there are distractions. Remember that even with the sound turned down, television pictures will be distracting to both parties
> - Use long complicated sentences
> - Talk about doing something long before you do it. This can lead to anticipatory anxiety, particularly if it involves something like going to the dentist
> - Assume that pronouns like 'he', 'she' or 'it' will be clear to the person
> - Keep repeating something if you are misunderstood
> - Use gestures that could be seen as threatening.

Remember, however, that communication is about more than techniques. It is about relationships, developing trust, showing respect, and attending as well as listening.

The need to attend to the meaning behind the words is critical. Because the person has lost the ability to find the correct words and phrases, they will often use words, phrases and even music that convey their feelings and meaning obliquely.

We need to listen beyond the literal and try and hear what is being communicated.

John Killick has done some excellent work on listening to the meaning behind the apparently disjointed and rambling talk of people with dementia. He has recorded these incoherent ramblings and then shown how, taken as a whole and as an expression of feeling, the person can be seen to be communicating a great deal (Killick 1994). The onus, of course, is on us to understand what is being communicated and not on the other person to make themselves clear to us.

The following poem is a good example.

THE BARROW

Have you seen my barrow?
I joined the group,
and now it belongs to all of us
But I don't know where it's gone.

It seems as if
I'm like a buzzing toy –
it buzzes round and round
but it doesn't mean much.
Recently I've been using
the large barrow
but it hasn't
taken all the work away.

But I go straight,
that's about the limit of it.
Altogether you won't find
much toing and froing
and doing or being
with me, I never carry
as full as you do.

The way this country's going
men can just go round and do as they choose.
They can take my bed
and my barrow.

I think I just drift about
I think that's what I do usually
I'm just a kind of quiet nobody.

While we can never be certain that we have fully understood what this man is saying, it is clear that he is talking about losses and his present sense of powerlessness. To dismiss this as rambling would not only be cruel it would also mean that an opportunity was lost to help the man express his feelings and to talk about a time when he was a 'somebody'.

This need to see behind the words is even more important with people with Down's syndrome who may have a smaller vocabulary to call on.

The man who every morning says *'I have to get my mother's paper'*, even though his mother has been dead for many years, may well be saying *'I want things to be how they used to be'*, or *'I want to be useful'*. He may be struggling to express a sense of loss about his mother or a feeling of uselessness.

The following chart is a useful way of trying to analyse what is being said:

What is said/done	Concealed meaning	Underlying feelings
A man with Alzheimer's Disease and Down's syndrome shouts 'I'm going home, I hate this place, you can't keep me here.' He then urinates on the floor	I want the toilet. I can't find it. Tell me where it is	Fear Agitation Anger Embarassment
A woman with Down's syndrome and Alzheimer's disease whose mother died many years ago keeps calling out to her and looking for her	I am alone I feel lost	Fear Sadness Frustration

We can only guess at the hidden meaning and feelings but at least stop and consider the possibility that the person's words may not literally convey what they mean and feel.

Because people with Down's syndrome and Alzheimer's disease have difficulty both using and understanding the spoken word, then we must pay more attention to non-verbal ways of communicating. Malcolm Goldsmith in *'Hearing the Voice of People with Dementia'* comments:

'It is probable that many opportunities are missed because carers are not sufficiently skilled in recognising and interpreting non-verbal communication.'

He further comments:

'Whilst many people recognise the value of non-verbal communication, there is little evidence that it is widely promoted or used in dementia care.'

(Goldsmith 1996)

TOUCH

Touch is a fundamental form of communication, which we all use even when our verbal skills are intact. For someone whose ability to find the right word or phrase is impaired touch becomes even more important. For someone who is visually or hearing impaired the possibility of both becoming and feeling isolated increases. Touch is a way of making contact.

For people working with people with Down's syndrome there is a particular hurdle here. Very often workers have been involved in helping people use touch appropriately. If you have been involved in trying to stop someone hugging and kissing at the wrong times it can be difficult to then start to increase touching. This is especially problematic if other people with learning difficulties are in the same house but being given different messages.

People with Alzheimer's disease become easily agitated and then more confused. Touch is a way of reducing stress. This can of course be done in planned ways through the use of hand and foot massage, but it is sad to reflect that this might be the only way someone gets such a fundamental human need met.

There is a need to recognise that touch can be abusive or at least offensive to people in various settings and situations. However, if this is kept in mind, workers could and should use touch both to help with relaxation and as an aid to communication.

Creating a therapeutic environment

As noted earlier the activities of daily living are affected early in the development of Alzheimer's disease. Despite their apparent ordinariness, most activities of daily living require complex patterns of behaviour and cognitions that use different parts of the brain.

Take for example the apparently simple activity of putting on the kettle to make a cup of tea:

● Go to the kitchen	We have to remember the layout of the house: this involves our right side frontal lobe. We also use our cerebellum to control our motor skills of walking and balancing.
● Pick up the kettle	We have to recognise the kettle, using our right side temporal lobe, and then understand what has to be done with it
● Fill the kettle	We have to recognise taps and also concentrate on not over-filling it. The initiator in our frontal lobes needs to maintain the energy to turn on and off appropriately
● Turn it on and leave to boil	This requires recognition of the switch. Short term memory, which uses frontal lobes, is necessary to remind us to return when the kettle has boiled.

The danger is that the care giver takes over the whole task. But clearly parts of the brain are still functioning. A therapeutic model demands that the person with Alzheimer's disease is encouraged to maintain those skills still available to them. They may still be able to recognise the kettle if you give it to them and may be able to fill it up if you tell them when to stop.

In Alzheimer's disease the brain is going to deteriorate and eventually all parts will be damaged. What we must not do is do the work for those parts still left in tact. If we do that we are only serving to speed up the process of deterioration and loss.

It is important to find the correct balance between giving the person support to do what they can do and making them do what they find too difficult and stressful. Equally one needs to recognise that the person may simply not want to do the task; perhaps it is boring for them and they would not have wanted to do it whether they had dementia or not.

What carers and workers need to do, then, is create an environment which facilitates the maintenance of as many skills as possible for as long as possible.

This requires constant monitoring and vigilance. People with Down's syndrome and Alzheimer's disease tend to experience quite sudden and rapid changes. These need responding to promptly.

The majority of people with Down's syndrome and Alzheimer's disease live at home with a carer. Social workers have a role to play in advising the carer of ways to adapt the environment to make life easier and less frustrating for all concerned.

Social workers are also involved in advising carers of suitable placements. Carers often comment that what they want from social workers is someone who can advise them of the merits and disadvantages of particular residential, nursing, community or day care provision.

Social workers are, of course, also involved in staffing the various care settings and providing care and support.

Social workers need to know what to look for and what to provide.

ASPECTS OF THE ENVIRONMENT

Because people with Alzheimer's disease have difficulty with visual and cognitive functioning they are unable to prioritise or shut out stimuli. They do not know what to pay attention to. The result is that environments can be over-stimulating and trigger anxiety and confusion.

This is a particular problem for people with Down's syndrome and Alzheimer's disease living in supported accommodation with other people with learning disabilities. The remit for good practice in these environments is to provide a setting which maximises the potential of everyone; the aim is to encourage growth and therefore change. Quite rightly in this environment, workers and carers are engaged in providing as much stimulus as possible to help people grow and take on new challenges and skills to become as independent as possible. This environment can be too demanding for the person with Alzheimer's disease.

An added problem is that because the person also has difficulty triggering their own activities and stimuli, environments can also become under-stimulating, with the same confusing effect.

Environments must therefore be:

- Predictable
- Calm
- Make sense
- Structured
- Suitably stimulating
- Familiar

- Because the world is becoming unpredictable and confusing, daily routines should be maintained as far as possible. Carry out dressing, washing and eating at the same times and in the same places. Also try to have the same person involved.
- Avoid making unnecessary changes. Redecorating may brighten the place up but will cause added confusion.
- Try not to use the same space for different activities. If the dining room is used for craft work or dancing and the lounge for Sunday worship it is easy for cues to be misinterpreted and the place cease to make sense.
- Use music. Music can be very calming. It is important to use appropriate music. Do not use music as a constant backdrop to the day, as the continuous noise only adds clutter to the environment and will cause stress and added confusion.
- If there are gatherings of people arrange for the person with dementia to be given individual attention. The increased noise and activity will frighten and frustrate them, and they will need the security of someone's company.
- The person needs to be helped to orientate themselves. This means removing or camouflaging triggers that will decrease orientation and encourage inappropriate behaviour, and emphasising those triggers that will help orientation.

● Someone with Alzheimer's disease has difficulty differentiating colours, especially those at the bottom end of the spectrum. Colours from the top end of the spectrum, such as red, orange and yellow, are much more noticeable; therefore painting toilet doors bright colours can aid recognition. Conversely it is useful to camouflage a door that you do not want used: put a plant in front of it or paint it the same colour as the wall – although this can give the illusion that people are appearing through the wall! As with all decisions it is necessary to balance gains against losses. Painting the doors may well cause confusion initially but unlike a complete redecoration should in the end be more orientating than confusing.

● Because the person will respond uncritically to a trigger, the sight of a door is an open invitation to go outside. Fire doors can be the source of much anxiety for staff as people are drawn towards them and the outside. Again there is a need to change the trigger. Make the door look like a window: cover the bottom half with dark cloth and hang curtains on the top half so it looks like a window. (Fire regulations will permit this as long as the push bar is exposed.) This treatment can also be given to doors in people's own homes. It is a good example of the need to do a risk assessment when working with people with dementia; certainly it is wrong to create a situation where the person never takes any risks, but the debate is around the level of acceptable risk. I worked with a staff group who were at the point of moving a woman into secure nursing accommodation because she went out of the fire door up to eight times a day. After adapting the door to look like a window the woman stopped going out that way, and was able to continue living in the home until her death.

● Use visual cues as much as possible. If the person can read it is useful to label things. For many people with Down's syndrome this isn't an option, and even if it is in the early stages of Alzheimer's disease, it is a skill which soon goes. Using pictures, though, is extremely useful. Remember that the picture has to have meaning for the person and it also has to be visible. It needs, therefore, to be at the person's eye level. This may well be considerably lower than the carer's eye level, especially if the person is using a Zimmer or is in a wheelchair.

- Consider mirrors. People with Alzheimer's disease find it difficult to recognise themselves in the mirror or indeed to realise that the image in the mirror is only an image and not another person. They may complain that people keep coming into their room, especially at night. This may well be because of reflections in large mirrors. One man I know of had a full length mirror on his wardrobe and a mirror on the wall. His nights were times of trauma and distress. Once the mirrors were covered at night he returned to calm nights. For the same reason it is worth using non-glare glass on pictures.

- Lighting also warrants attention. People in the middle stages of Alzheimer's disease tend to become more confused and disorientated as the light fades. This is called 'Sundowning'. You need to turn the lights on at least two hours before sunset. For carers who are already stretched it is useful to have a timer so that the lights come on automatically.

- Try to use non-glare lighting to eliminate confusing shadows.

- Use flooring with a dull, non-shiny finish. Shiny surfaces can very easily look like water or even a pit. One man I know of suddenly refused to go to the bathroom despite having always been fastidious about his washing. Staff reported that he would walk happily to the bathroom door and then jam his hands against the door posts and refuse to go any further. It transpired that the floor was covered in shiny vinyl. He thought it was a pool of water that he would fall into.

- Because people with Alzheimer's disease have difficulty with three-dimensional vision, attention should be given to changes in the colour of the carpets specifically and flooring generally. Consider the following: -

  James had lived in his supported accommodation for five years. One day he suddenly froze and became very agitated on his way into the house via the back door. Staff tried patiently to coax him but he became more and more agitated and started to cry.

  The cover to the drain which extended across most of the passageway to the back door had been painted red. To James it looked like a deep hole!

- Maintaining a suitably stimulating environment is important throughout the process of the disease but requires particular attention in the mid stages. Failure-free activities should be built into the daily routine. More information on these can be found in *'Activities I and II'* (Archibald 1990 and 1993).

Some places have found the use of Snoezaleen rooms therapeutic, especially in the mid stages. These provide a relaxing but stimulating environment. They are, however, expensive and there is some evidence that the long term effects may be no more marked than if a calm environment with suitable music, aromas and gentle activity is provided.

All the above suggestions facilitate a calm, predictable environment that makes as much sense as possible, but they are only the backdrop against which individualised, holistic support and caring should exist. On their own they are nowhere near enough.

Maintaining skills

The activities of daily living in which we all, apparently, so easily engage involve, as indicated earlier, the use of many different parts of the brain. The simple instruction to *'Collect your coat from the hall and put it on'* involves first the parietal lobe in order to understand the words. The hypothalamus then provides the memory of what needs to be done, the cerebellum co-ordinates the voluntary movements of walking, and the temporal lobe is used to think through the process of making the right decisions.

For someone with Alzheimer's disease this can be a demanding task, but for someone who already has impaired learning this can be almost too much. The temptation is to do the work for the person. What is effectively happening if we do this is that we are speeding up the process of deterioration. Some parts of the brain are still left to function and must be encouraged to work. The saying *'Use it or lose it'* is especially relevant here. Always we must work to maintain as many skills as possible. It is important, however, to get the correct balance between supporting someone to maintain a skill and forcing them to do something that is too demanding or has already been lost to function.

Sometimes, when a number of skills are disappearing at the same time, it can be difficult to know how to prioritise. The needs of the person can appear to be overwhelming and there may even be pressure to move the person to another setting. However, when someone's adaptive skills are diminishing one of their principle needs is to have as much control over their environment as possible.

This requires that they are maintained in their familiar environment for as long as possible. The environment also needs to be adapted and systems put in place that help them maintain the skills that are needed for them to remain in control for as long as possible.

Of course it may not be possible to manage to meet all of the person's needs. An assessment of which are the most significant is therefore the first step. This should be done as far as possible with the person and in particular has to take into account the principles of assessment identified earlier. In deciding on priorities of need it is important to be aware of how and why your decisions are based on the respective notions of 'substituted judgement' and 'best interest'.

Having made decisions about which skills to give priority to, a system which makes certain that there is consistent practice by all staff needs to be put in place. If the practice is not consistent the environment becomes unpredictable and exacerbates the person's confusion and general distress.

One way to do this is through the use of 'Goal Plans'.

GOAL PLANS

A goal plan is a plan developed in negotiation with the client, staff and carer. It is a tool to analyse and break down a task into its component parts and is used to systematically teach and maintain skills.

Essentially it also provides a system which ensures continuity and consistency of support and care, giving the person maximum opportunity to predict and control their daily living and therefore maintain skills.

Below is an example of a goal plan which was used to help a man with Down's syndrome and Alzheimer's disease maintain the skill of shaving. It also provided a record of his progress and allowed his key worker and the staff group to determine where he needed most support.

GOAL PLAN
Name: Peter

O = Independently
1 = Verbal prompt
2 = Physical prompt
3 = Do task for person
4 = Person did not want to do the task

Praise: Appropriate behaviour
Ignore: Inappropriate behaviour
Mark: Type of prompt to attain appropriate behaviour

Goal: To enable Peter to continue to shave himself

	A	B	C	D	E	F
1	Staff initials	DC				
2	Date	16/5/98				
3	Verbal Prompt to put plug in	1				
4	Physical prompt to run water	2				
5	Both check water temp.	3				
6	Verbal prompt to open foam	1				
7	Physical prompt to apply foam	2				
8	Verbal prompt to wet razor	1				
9	Physical prompt to shave	2				
10	Left side of face	2				
11	Right side of face	2				
12	Under chin	2				
13	Below mouth	3				
14	Below nose	3				
15	Verbal prompt to look in mirror	1				
16	Repeat above if needed	1				
17	Verbal prompt to wash off foam	0				
18	Verbal prompt to dry face	0				

With support, people with dementia may be able to relearn some old skills with some success. Many people with Down's syndrome may not have had the extensive repertoire of skills that others have had, but they will certainly have had some skills. The problem for many social workers working in community settings is that they may not have very extensive histories available to them to give information about these past skills and abilities. People with Down's syndrome who have spent much of their lives in long stay hospital often come out with little information about their past. The information that is available is often only for the last few years and tells little of past hobbies and activities that the person had twenty years previously. It is critical that at the point of moving out into the community, workers find out as much as possible from staff and other users about people's past lives. It is, of course, equally important when people move from home to residential care. Social workers need to develop as full a picture as possible of the person's history, interests and past skills.

The maintenance of skills is, however, only possible in a milieu which aids concentration and reduces stress, and which values relationships and people's emotional well-being. A concentration on achievement will lead to confrontation, stress and damage to self esteem. As with all of us, although to a much greater extent for people with Alzheimer's disease, there are optimum times for achieving things. Something that is not possible in the morning may well be achievable in the afternoon or on another day.

This is particularly relevant to carers who may well feel despair and frustration when a previously achieved task is not completed. It may be that the disease has progressed to the point where the function is lost for ever. It may be that the person has been over-stimulated, is tired or simply wants to do something else. They may also simply be exercising their right to choose. They may well be perfectly able and willing to do it at another time.

> 'Successful care-giving promotes positive emotions. It is measured by the confrontations avoided, not by the tasks accomplished! What didn't work today may well work tomorrow.'
>
> **(Antonangeli 1995)**

Specific interventions

The level of disability experienced is not simply the product of the disease but is also the result of the influence of the environment. This can either mitigate or exacerbate the disabling effects of the disease. The environment is, of course, more than just that which is built around us. It is the milieu in which relationships are made, expectations conveyed and emotions acknowledged.

Whilst it is clearly important to know about different approaches, their validity and impact, it is important to note that they are only techniques and only as good as the person who uses them. No single approach is a panacea. There are simply some identified ways of working which enhance the person's quality of life and against which practice can be described and evaluated.

The approaches to be considered here are:

- Reality orientation
- Validation
- Reminiscence work
- Music
- Aromatherapy.

REALITY ORIENTATION

Reality Orientation (R.O.) is a tool for helping people maintain skills, relearn old skills where possible, retain as much control as possible over their environment, and improve generally the quality of their lives.

In this context, then, it is essential to see R.O. as a stress reducer and not as a source of anxiety or boredom. Where R.O. is restricted to orientation to date, time, names and weather through the use of signboards (often not looked at!) and calendars, people are going to get bored. Care providers also need to ask themselves about the quality of relationships that exist if this is the main focus and method of orientation. Why are people told what the weather is like when they could experience it for themselves either by looking out of the window or going outside and then discussing it?

Thought also needs to be given to the quality of present realities. Why orientate someone to a reality which is painful and from which they gain no long term insight or relief? The person who every morning awakens and becomes agitated saying *'I must go and get my mother's breakfast'* will only be caused intense grief if reminded that their mother is dead – a grief which will not lead to resolution or insight because the dementia prevents the storing of the information.

There is, however, an important role for R.O. if it is geared to the needs of individual personality, skills, abilities and needs.

Those who have been working with people with learning disabilities will probably be familiar with using visual cues to orientate people. With the onset of dementia verbal communication becomes increasingly difficult and cuing with pictures or patterns and colours should be used. It is important to use cues that make sense to the person. For example, someone whose short term memory is failing may well not respond to a modern symbol for a toilet but may recognise an old cistern with a chain. Similarly they may recognise a picture of themselves when young but not as they are now.

Using orientating cues in the conversation is more useful than relying only on written information. For people with Down's syndrome their ability to use written cues will be considerably limited compared to the general population with Alzheimer's disease. Saying *'Today is Wednesday. On Wednesday we go to...'* will orientate to the day as will the repetition of relevant names.

Many will, however, have learned a sign language such as Makaton and more recently Signalong. Workers who have been working with people with learning disabilities may well know these lanugages already, but other workers should consider learning this form of communication in order to help with orientation. To find out more about these forms of communication workers need to contact the speech and language therapists at their local hospital or health centre.

Of course the physical environment is also critical in facilitating orientation. Points made earlier about the need for buildings and their uses to make sense are relevant here. The building should make finding rooms and direction easy. Very often people become disorientated because the room they need is not visible or indicated in any way and they then become lost.

R.O. is most useful when it is embedded in significant relationships and is a thread running through people's daily living. It can also be provided as a group activity. This of course also provides extra stimulation and encourages the person to engage in a world that is diminishing for them. There needs, however, to be a constant monitoring to guard against over-stimulation, which will serve to increase anxiety.

Research shows that whilst the progression of the disease cannot be impeded, the use of activities and orientation can mitigate some of the effects and therefore slow down the clinical symptoms.

(For a more detailed account of the use of R.O. see Una Holden's chapter in *'Working with Dementia'*, Stokes and Goudie 1990.)

VALIDATION

This is a way of working which gives validity to the other person's perception of reality.

To return to the person who wakes every morning anxious to make their mother's breakfast: far from being helpful, reminding them that their mother is dead will actually be experienced as a cruel reminder of a loss. Validation work acknowledges that the person with dementia is experiencing a different reality and that they may well be better staying there, at least temporarily.

A problem for carers and workers is that they do not want to lie or play 'lets pretend'. If someone is talking about their mother then you do so as well, but maintaining the past tense *'What did your mother like for breakfast?'*, *'What did you cook?'* etc. The person will often start to use the past tense themselves and will usually become less agitated. It is then much easier to introduce some type of diversion. One of the benefits of the disease as far as workers and carers are concerned is that people have a short memory span and once relaxed will be easily distracted.

You also need to attend to the feelings and the meaning behind the words spoken. The person may be expressing a distress that things are no longer how they used to be. They may want to feel useful and know that they still have an importance.

It is, of course, good practice to 'go at the clients pace' and to 'walk beside the client'. Because we find it more difficult to do this when someone has dementia, we have to try harder. It is worth reflecting on the fact that if we find it hard to enter their reality when our brains are functioning well, how much more difficult is it for the person with dementia to enter our reality?

REMINISCENCE

From about the age of 10 years children will start to reminisce. It is an activity that we constantly engage in from then on. Apart from linking us to others and making us feel good, it is actually an important part of our mental health. It is through our history that we know who we are, what has formed us. It gives us our place in the world and therefore our identity.

For someone with a dual diagnosis the past may not only be more familiar but may well be a more relaxing place to be. For some people the past may have painful memories. For many people with Down's syndrome the past may involve unexplained changes and losses as well as the experiences of long stay hospitalisation and institutionalised care.

However, the evidence is that reminiscence is a positive experience and workers should facilitate it.

This can be done in a number of ways:

- **Group Activities** Here the facilitator can use triggers such as old photos, pictures of old equipment, videos of events and music from the past. People are encouraged to reminisce about the times pictured and discussed. This activity not only encourages a sense of the past but also encourages sharing amongst the group.
- **One-to-one work** For many people with Down's syndrome and Alzheimer's disease the group will be over-stimulating. It will be hard for them to feel in

continued...

> ...*continued*
>
> control of what is going on. One-to-one reminiscence can be done using the same stimuli or using more personal memorabilia. Visiting old familiar places can be a great trigger to the past.
>
> ● **Life story work** This involves the compilation of a record of the person's life, but the process is probably more important than the product. This is not about getting together a history book. It is about working with someone to help them remember their past and to help them share it with significant others. It can involve compiling photographs, pictures from magazines, collecting significant objects, such as ornaments, programmes, postcards, etc. These belong to the person involved and should be seen as personal and confidential.

The added benefit of this type of work is that it gives a focus for communication and, where carers know little of the person's previous life, it helps to fill out information about hobbies, interests, significant events and relationships. A more holistic view of the person will emerge. This is especially important as the person can become seen as increasingly fragmented.

Music

Music engages us sensually and emotionally. It is also a way in which many people choose to relax and deal with stress. For those whose cognitive functions are deteriorating the use of music can be at least as important and arguably more significant in their experience of relaxation and pleasure.

Music can be used formally as a therapeutic tool or simply as part of a relaxing and pleasure-giving environment. When deciding how, when and what music to use, carers and workers may find the following findings and experiences useful:

> ● Malcolm Goldsmith in *'Hearing the Voice of People with Dementia'* (1996) refers to the work of a music therapist who used percussion instruments and 'a careful selection of music... to mirror the various moods of people, and enable them to "own" feelings that had been repressed.'
> ● A study carried out in Sweden of 25 nursing home patients with dementia found that they were 'less irritable, anxious and depressed and ate more when music was played during dinner.' (Ragsnoskog 1994)
>
> *continued...*

...continued

- Prinsley (1986) found that music memory tended to be fixed during the ages of 15-25 years. This is, therefore, the music which will be most familiar and easiest to recall. The study was not of people with Down's syndrome and Alzheimer's disease so it is possible that there may be a different age for 'fixing' in these people. Nevertheless the recognition of the fixing is significant. Carers need to find out which music is best fixed and most significant. For many people with Down's syndrome the music they heard at the music-fixing stage in their life may not be the same as that of their peers but may well be the music listened to by their parent's generation. This certainly helps to explain why Doris Day is a favourite with a woman with a dual diagnosis whose adolescence spanned the 1960s. Does it also help to explain why people of the same age who were in large institutions at that time prefer Scottish country dancing music?
- Music that has positive memories can also be helpful in the management of challenging behaviour.
- Fast tempo music increases energy levels. It should not be used if someone is agitated. If someone is agitated use calming music. This is particularly relevant when people are pacing or wandering about in an agitated state.
- It may be better in the evenings to play tunes but not songs. People sometimes wake in the night saying that they can hear the words of the song going round in their heads.
- A constant backdrop of music may simply add clutter to the environment and cause increased agitation.
- Music should be be tailored to the needs of individuals. The process of finding out which music is significant and why can be part of the development of life story work.
- Very often people who have lost the ability to hold a coherent conversation will be able to sing the entire words of a song. This is of course very rewarding for them. It is also possible for the person to be 'conversed' with by others singing with them.

AROMATHERAPY

Aromatherapy has proved to be particularly therapeutic for people with Alzheimer's disease, particularly in its mid stage. One of the most important challenges at this stage is to maintain appropriate levels of communication and stimulation. Smells can be evocative and stimulate memories which then encourage people to talk.

Certain oils are also useful in managing behaviour. Lavender, for example, reduces anxiety and aids relaxation. The effect of this is to reduce confusion and, interestingly, use of the oil can help where the ability to speak clearly is being lost. This is of particular relevance to people with Down's syndrome.

Where mobility is decreasing a massage with lavender oil can help the relaxation of the limb muscles. One of the best-tried uses of lavender is as an aid to sleep. For people with Alzheimer's disease who are experiencing disturbed sleep patterns, lavender oil has sometimes had quite dramatic results.

More detailed information can be found in *'Aromatherapy for People with Dementia'* (Reed 1996). This provides a general introduction, some do's and don'ts, and a brief lesson in hand massage.

Challenging behaviour

> *'"Challenging behaviour" is a term used to describe behaviour that we find difficult to deal with. It upsets us or makes us feel uncomfortable or threatened. It is behaviour which challenges us.*
> *The challenge is to understand the feelings, needs and intentions behind the behaviour and to find ways of working that do not punish the person.'*
> **(Cairns and Kerr 1994)**

Unlike the general population with Alzheimer's disease, the person with a dual diagnosis may not only exhibit new challenging behaviours but may also experience the re-emergence of previously modified challenging behaviours. Someone who twenty years previously had learned not to kiss and touch everyone they met but has now lost twenty years of memory may well re-engage in that behaviour.

It is important to recognise that although the behaviour may seem random and inexplicable to us, the person is actually responding to a trigger that sets off the behaviour. We also need to recognise that the person is trying to communicate with us.

The challenge for us is to try to:

- Discover what the trigger is
- Understand what the emotions are behind the behaviour
- Understand what the person is trying to communicate
- Understand the meaning of the behaviour
- Put ourselves in their shoes and see the world from their perspective.

Consider the following:

> Imagine you are sitting in your sitting room and a stranger comes in and starts to move things about and even opens cupboard doors and takes things out before going into the kitchen apparently to repeat the performance.

What would your feelings be and what would you do?

It doesn't take much imagination to get in touch with feelings of anger, fear, panic and a sense of threat.

Presumably you would engage in some fight or flight activity – a perfectly normal response to feeling threatened in this way. You may shout for help, shout at the intruder, physically defend yourself or freeze in fear.

A person with Alzheimer's disease may not understand what is happening to them. If they don't know who you are, where they are or the reasons for what you are doing, then they may become frightened, panicked, frustrated and angry. It is then possible that they will try to stop whatever it is that is happening to them, in exactly the same way as anyone else would.

Remember that the person with Alzheimer's disease cannot modify their behaviour. You have to modify yours, or modify the environment if the trigger is there.

The danger is that we label the person as aggressive and see this as an inevitable aspect of the progression of the disease, rather than seeing it as an effect and then seeking out the cause.

To avoid this we need to use our imagination and always think of as many explanations of a particular challenging behaviour as possible. The person with Alzheimer's disease will not be able to explain the reasons behind their behaviour, and so we need to know as much as possible about them and their past if we are going to make sense of it.

For many people with Down's syndrome, institutions may have been the places where they spent much of their lives. Consequently there is often a lack of information about their history and background, and what is available is often fragmented.

The following case study provides a useful example of the reasons why and how a lack of background information can lead to an incorrect assessment and understanding of the person's behaviour.

Mr Carpenter is 49 years old and has lived in supported accommodation for five years after spending most of his life in a large institution. Mr Carpenter has Down's syndrome and Alzheimer's disease.

For the last few weeks he has become agitated most evenings around tea time. He has started pushing the person who is making a pot of tea. He pushes them and then grabs the pot off them. Recently, the pot fell to the floor during the incident and smashed.

Once he has the pot, he makes the tea and then puts the kettle in the cupboard. If another tenant goes to the cupboard at this time they are verbally abused by Mr Carpenter. It seems that staff are allowed to touch the teapot and can go into the cupboard without Mr Carpenter bothering about it. Once tea is over, he becomes less agitated.

Adapted from '*Different Realities*' (Cairns and Kerr 1994)

The explanation for Mr Carpenter's behaviour is rooted in his past. He had been responsible for making the tea when he was in hospital. If he failed to do so, he was scolded by the staff. He was frightened that if someone else made the tea, he would get into serious trouble. It was his responsibility, it was an important job, it was one of the few occasions when he felt valued.

It is reasonable to assume that the trigger of tea being made caused him anxiety and set off a response which was not related to the present but to previous behaviour. Because of his loss of memory the imperative to make the tea became a present fact and not a thing of the past.

Without the knowledge about Mr Carpenter's responsibilities many years ago he could easily have been seen as behaving irrationally and as an aggressive person.

ASSESSING THE SITUATION

One of the dangers in trying to understand the meaning behind a person's behaviour is that we jump to conclusions. There is a temptation to form a quick assessment of the cause of a particular piece of behaviour. But because the person cannot explain the reasons themselves, we need to be extremely cautious about imposing a simple and apparently obvious explanation.

As with all assessments, information needs to be gathered over time and dealt with systematically.

A useful model for doing this is the A.B.C. system of behavioural analysis.

This provides an opportunity to record all of the elements which interact to create a challenging situation.

Any violent or unsettling situation will involve a complex interaction of the environment, the person involved, their history, personality and needs, and the carer or worker.

How does A.B.C. work.?

Basically it is a way of organising information under the following headings:

A Activating event	Who was around at the time or just before the event? When did the event occur? Where did the behaviour occur? What was the person doing immediately before the event?
B Behaviour	Is this behaviour new? What form did it take? Was it verbal or physical? What words did the person use? What or who was the target of the behaviour? How long did it last?
C Consequences	How did others respond to the event? Was the person told off, ignored, sedated or restrained? How did the person respond to the way others approached the event?

This information needs to be recorded systematically. The following chart kept over a three-week period can provide a good summary and overview:

Time and Date	A	B	C	Background

It is suggested that that this is kept over three weeks to allow for changes in staffing, routines, weekends and other occurrences that might not happen every week.

The following check list provides a starting point when considering possible explanations:

- Is the environment over-stimulating?
- Is the environment under-stimulating?
- Does the person know who you are?
- Do they feel de-skilled?
- Do they feel out of control of their environment?
- Do they have sensory impairment? Particularly with people with Down's syndrome it is necessary to check hearing and visual loss
- Is there poor lighting which makes misinterpretation of stimuli more likely?
- Are they in pain?

DEALING WITH THE SITUATION

Once the situation has occurred it is important to deal with it as calmly as possible. Here are some useful do's and don'ts:

DO	DON'T
• Stay calm	• Confront the person
• Avoid invading the personal space	• Shout or raise your voice
• Touch the person gently, but make sure they see you first	• Touch or move in a manner indicating an attempt to control
• Use gentle calming music	• Move rapidly, especially from behind
• Turn off any music that has an insistent or agitating beat or noise level	• Tease, ridicule or use restraints
• Give plenty of room	• Show fear, alarm or anxiety
• Reassure no harm will come	• Corner the person
• Listen: encourage talk rather than action	• Provoke a catastrophic reaction
• Remove any audience	
• Divert attention	

Adrenalin stays in the body for up to 90 minutes after arousal. This means that even though things may seem to have calmed down everyone involved in the situation is still primed to react to any new threat or assumed attack. There needs to be specific attention paid to calming the environment and avoiding any behaviours or suggestions that may be perceived as dangerous.

If there does not appear to be any reasonable explanation other than the stage of the disease then medication may be indicated. However this should only be used after all other possible avenues have been explored and in the knowledge that many behavioural problems are of short duration. Medication should be regularly reviewed. It is also important to balance the benefits of the drug against possible side effects and to be clear about the impact of the challenging behaviour itself. Is it really so bad that there is no possibility of managing it in some other way?

There are, of course, many other challenging behaviours which may well require slightly different responses. The basic principles, however, still apply:

- Do not jump to quick interpretations
- Do try to see the world from the other person's perspective. Realise that their world is confused and may not be in your present but in their past.
- Look for triggers in the environment
- Manage your own behaviour
- Don't take it personally
- Seek support, advice and supervision.

Wandering or walking about

Mary is 50 years old. She has Down's syndrome and developed Alzheimer's disease about two years ago. Mary used to work from 9am to 5pm in a cafe where she was responsible for keeping the counter refilled and clearing the tables. She derived an enormous amount of pleasure and a sense of self-worth from this occupation. She derived most satisfaction from the opportunities it gave her to meet new people, make a widening circle of friends and earn money for clothes.

With the onset of the dementia it became increasingly difficult for Mary to continue to work at the cafe. Her memory loss and agitation was exacerbated by the constant toing and froing of customers and by the level of noise created by people talking and the clatter of china and cutlery, a situation made worse by the constant background musak.

Mary has spent an increasing amount of time at the house where she lives with three other people.

Over the last few months Mary has started to leave the house after breakfast. She sets off often in a slightly agitated state rushing to get her coat on and filling her handbag to bursting point. She does not tell anyone she is going.

The staff who are worried about Mary's lack of road sense and disorientation then set off down the road to get her back. This invariably results in a public scene with Mary becoming increasingly agitated.

Staff are concerned that Mary has now started 'wandering' and that this is the result of the inevitable progression of the disease.

In order to understand the meaning behind the behaviour and therefore develop an appropriate management response, carers and workers need to ask the following questions:

- What was the purpose of the behaviour?
- What was the trigger for the behaviour?
- What did the person achieve by engaging in this behaviour?

There are many possible explanations for someone wandering or walking about. Most of the reasons are indicators of purpose. There is a temptation to see wandering behaviour in people with dementia as purposeless. This is usually directly attributable to the fact that we do not understand the purpose, and not that there is no purpose. Our interpretation is, of course, made more likely because the person cannot explain to us the reason for their behaviour.

Consider the following possible explanations:

- **Disorientation** This can occur on arrival at a new place. The person may be trying to orientate themselves. They may be trying to find significant places, such as toilets and bedrooms. A person with Down's syndrome will probably take longer to process this information.
- **Physical discomfort** People may well go for a walk to relieve discomfort and pain. This may be caused, for example, by constipation or arthritis. Remember that people with Down's syndrome sometimes have difficulty in expressing their pain and discomfort.
- **Boredom** All of us become bored and restless if we do not have sufficient exercise and stimulation. This does not change because someone has Down's syndrome and Alzheimer's disease. By giving sufficient opportunities for physical activities the incidence of so-called wandering decreases dramatically in any individual. The fact that someone's mobility is impaired is not a reason to cut down on these activities. The experience of going for a walk in a wheelchair is still stimulating!
- **Searching** This can occur when someone is looking for someone or some place that is lost to them. This is of course a normal part of grieving. The person with Alzheimer's disease may be searching for someone lost to them many years ago but their memory loss means that they have returned to the earlier stage of grieving.
- **Separation anxiety** The person may be anxious about losing someone. Because of the short term memory loss they may forget for how long the other person has been gone, or may have forgotten a promise by that person to return soon.
- **Re-activated previous activities** Triggers in the environment which connect with past activities may lead the person to believe that they are back in that past life and that there is an imperative to engage in whatever the activity was. Re-activated commitments to work or other well-learned routines are common. Clearly the work routine will often involve leaving the home and going outside.

continued...

…continued

- **Night-time wandering** The likelihood of this occurring is increased because of the lack of information in the environment to help the person orientate themselves and keep in touch with reality. The darkness may also cause shadows and mirrors create reflections that will frighten the person. This will increase their agitation and their feeling of a need to get away.
- **Attention seeking** By engaging in wandering behaviour the person will call the attention of others to them.
- **Apparent aimlessness** The person may set off with a clear intention to go somewhere or do something but because of their short term memory loss will then forget the reason that they started the activity.

In trying to understand Mary's apparent wandering it would be useful to use the A.B.C. formula. This would pinpoint when it happened and what the possible triggers were in the environment. Given the case history it is likely that the trigger was the end of breakfast, perhaps, combined with a lack of other things to do and the feeling of agitation being interpreted as anxiety about being late for work at the cafe. There could of course be other explanations and a full life history as well as systematic recording of incidents would be the only way to arrive at a fairly reliable assessment.

Supporting carers

In a study carried out in Lanarkshire it was found that 50% of carers of people with learning disabilities were 60 years old and over, and 25% of these were between 65 and 74 years old (Irving 1992). Most of these carers were women. There is no reason to suppose this is not representative of the rest of the country.

Carers of people with a dual diagnosis are often elderly, are susceptible to the illnesses and frailties of older age and are also in the age group with an increased risk of developing Alzheimer's disease themselves. They are also likely to be single women, and this also puts them in a category that is particularly likely to experience low incomes and limited resources.

They will have coped with the demands of caring for someone with Down's syndrome and will very often experience the additional diagnosis of Alzheimer's disease as a cruel and unbearable blow. Many feel a gross unfairness in the onset of an additional burden, both for themselves and for their relative. For the care giver coping with someone who has Alzheimer's disease can lead to feelings that are part of grieving: anger, guilt and depression. Feelings of embarrassment and helplessness combined with the physical demands often lead to increasing isolation.

Because many carers of people with Down's syndrome have been involved with service providers for many years and are likely to have developed skills in negotiating for resources and articulating their needs, there is a danger that social workers will fail to recognise their vulnerability. In fact the carers are themselves more likely to feel that they should and could cope. The Lanarkshire study found that there was little correlation between the levels of service and the level of incapacity of the person with Down's syndrome.

By their middle years many people with Down's syndrome may have lost both parents. The responsibility for care then often passes on to the next female relative, usually a sister. These women are of course often caring for their own children and are balancing a burden of responsibility and care which leaves little energy to cope with the demands of an increasingly dependent relative with Alzheimer's disease.

Over the years the carer will have developed routines and coping strategies. With the inevitable changes that occur the carer needs to begin to adjust or even let go of previous ways of being and doing. This in itself is potentially very stressful.

Social workers need to work closely with carers and, as now required by legislation under the **Carer's Recognition and Services Act 1996**, carry out an assessment of their needs.

The following identifies some common and basic needs of carers:

- To be given a diagnosis as early as possible. There is a general reluctance to do this. This leaves carers without appropriate supports and they are denied the opportunity to make appropriate plans for the future.
- Full information about the likely course of the disease. Carers also need to know what changes are attributable to the development of the disease. Very often they are aware of changes but not of their significance. Carers often report retrospectively that a dramatic change occurred after a particular upheaval. Holidays seem to be a point at which changes in competence and personality are noted. A remark made by a carer that 'He was never the same again after the holiday' has echoes of other similar observations made by carers. Of course this requires early diagnosis and clear information about the way in which people with a dual diagnosis are affected.
- To be made aware of the significance of the interaction between the environment and the disease. Carers need to know how to use the environment to help counteract the impact of the disease.
- To be helped to allow their relative to maintain skills as far as possible. The carer needs to be supported in resisting the temptation to do things for the person that they can still do for themselves. For a carer who is under pressure and stressed, this is not easy.
- Support, which may be financial, particularly if there is a need for structural changes such as moving a bedroom downstairs or putting in another toilet.
- Help to understand and cope with difficulties caused by the changes, especially those which cause communication problems.

continued...

...continued

- Support and counselling to help them cope with feelings of loss. These will be needed in the early stages as well as later on. The loss of the person as they were known is a source of grief to carers. They need to be supported in this as well as in the final stages of dying and death.
- Information about available resources. This also involves the worker being able to give information about the suitability of various respite, day care and residential settings for people with a dual diagnosis. They need to be given information about services which will give them time out and opportunities to develop themselves. Social workers must have knowledge of all the local voluntary, private and statutory resources available. Carers report that this is the single most important contribution that the social worker can make. A deep sense of frustration is experienced when this is not available. Of course they often have to be helped to then utilise these services.
- Support in making difficult decisions about the care of their relative.

Conclusion

As discussed throughout this Practitioner's Guide, people with Down's syndrome and Alzheimer's disease have the same basic needs as anyone else. They do, however, have some specific needs which require a more responsive and tailored approach. They are likely to experience much more rapid changes in the progression of the disease than people in the general population. They therefore require more frequent reviews and assessments of need. They have fewer skills and abilities to draw on to help them mitigate the effects of the disease and will often have a more complex set of symptoms than the general population. More demands are made of the people working to support them.

At the moment people with Down's syndrome and Alzheimer's disease are often trapped by the label that they acquire. They are essentially seen as having a learning disability label which, in effect, excludes them from provision for people with dementia. This service may be inappropriate anyway, and where it is provided means that people in their middle age are placed with older adults in their seventies and eighties.

It may well be that what is required at the later stages is a specific service which provides hospice-type care. To date there is no such provision.

However, maintaining people in their familiar and comforting environment for as long as possible should be the focus of the work. This means that the environment has to be adapted. This can involve complex negotiations and sometimes considerable financial outlay.

What social workers are left with is a need to be vigilant in their observation of changes, anticipate and prepare for these and negotiate adaptations to present services. They need to support carers, providing them with training as well as counselling and advice.

Finally they need to be recording the existence of a particular area of unmet need which must be addressed if people with the dual diagnosis of Down's syndrome and

Alzheimer's disease are going to be provided with services that help them maintain their abilities and relationships for as long as possible, and are treated holistically and not just as a doubly labelled group.

A set of principles which should inform all work with people with a dual diagnosis can be summarised as follows. There should always be:

- A recognition of each individual's uniqueness

- The avoidance of stereotypical responses

- A holistic approach which sees the person first and the disease second

- Careful and multi-disciplinary assessments

- Assessments and practices which draw on people's abilities as well as recognise their needs

- Emphasis on familiarity and an avoidance of unnecessary change

- An adaptation of environments to respond to changing needs at different stages of the illness

- An emphasis on keeping carers fully informed and involved.

Bibliography

Antonangeli, J. (1995) *Of Two Minds*, Fidelity Press, Massachusetts.

Archibald, C. (1990 and 1993) *Activities I and II,* Dementia Services Development Centre, University of Stirling.

Aylward, E.H., Burt, D.B., Thorpe, M.D., Lai, F & Dalton, A.J. (1995) *Diagnosis of Dementia in Individuals with Intellectual Disability, Report of the American Association on Mental Retardation (AAMR)*, International Association for the Scientific Study of Intellectual Disability (IASSID), Working Group for the Diagnosis of Dementia in Individuals with Intellectual Disability

Burton, A., Chapman, A. and Myers, K. (1997) *Dementia: A Practice Guide for Social Workers,* Dementia Services Development Centre, University of Stirling.

Cairns, D. and Kerr, D. (1994) *Different Realities: A Training Guide for People with Down's Syndrome and Alzheimer's Disease*, Dementia Services Development Centre, University of Stirling.

Carenap D (1994) *Care Needs Assessment Pack for Dementia*, Crown Copyright, Dementia Services Development Centre, University of Stirling.

Dalton, A. J., Seltzer, G. B., Adlin, M. S. and Wisnieski, H. M. (1993) 'Association between Alzheimer's Disease and Down's Syndrome: Clinical Observations', in *Alzheimer's Disease, Down's Syndrome and their Relationship,* Ed. Berg, J. M., Karlinsky, H. and Holland, A. J., Oxford University Press

Dawson, B. (1994) *Common Symptomology Identified within Hansel Village*, Unpublished.

Gardner, I. (1993) *Dementia: New Skills for Social Workers*, Jessica Kingsley, London.

Goldsmith, M. (1996) *Hearing the Voice of People with Dementia: Opportunities and Obstacles,* Jessica Kingsley, London.

Hiles et al (1990) Down's Syndrome Group, *Western Pennsylvanian Newsletter* 8, pp. 27-30.

Irving, M. W. (1992) *The Effects of Ageing upon Individuals with Down's Syndrome*, Integrate News no 39 January

Jervis, G. (1948) 'Early Senile Dementia in Mongoloid Idiocy', *American Journal of Psychiatry*, vol 105, pp. 102-106.

Killick, J. (1994) *Please Give Me Back My Personality!: Writing and Dementia*, Dementia Services Development Centre, University of Stirling.

Koenig, B. R. (1995) *Current Gerontological Assessments and their Validity for Persons with an Intellectual Disability*, and *Aged and Dementia Care Issues for People with an Intellectual Disability*, vol 3, Minda Inc., Brighton, South Australia.

Lai, F. and Williams, R. S. (1989) 'A Prospective Study of Alzheimer's Disease in Down's Syndrome', *Archives of Neurology 1989*, vol 46, pp 849-53. Chicago

Murphy, E. (1986) *Dementia and Mental Illness in the Old*, Macmillan, London, p. 12.

Oswin, M. (1991) *Am I Allowed to Cry?*, Souvenir Press (Educational and Academic) Ltd, London and Canada.

Owens, D., Dawson, J. and Losin, C. (1971) 'Alzheimer's Disease in Down's Syndrome', *American Journal of Mental Deficiency*, vol 75, p 607.

Prasher, V. (1995) 'End-stage Dementia in Adults with Down's Syndrome', *International Journal of Geriatric Psychiatry*, vol 10, pp. 1067-9.

Prinsley, D. M. (1986) 'Music Therapy in Geriatric Care', *Australian Nurses Journal*, vol. 15, no. 9.

Ragnoskog, H. (1994) 'Dinner, Music and Dementia', in *Towards the Third Millenium: Conference Proceedings*, Adelaide Flinders Nurses Education and Research Funding, quoted in *Counselling Strategies*, Jane Granville-Short, Minda Inc., vol 2, Brighton, South Australia.

Reed, J. (1996) *Aromatherapy for People with Dementia*, Dementia Services Development Centre, University of Stirling.

Souner, R. and Desnoyers-Hurley, A. D. (1983) 'Do the Mentally Retarded Suffer from Affective Disorders?', *Archives of General Psychiatry*, vol 40, pp. 61-7.

Stokes, G. and Goudie, F. (1990) *Working with Dementia*, Winslow Press, Oxon.